A Treasure Cove Story

From the Movie

DISNEY
FROZEN

Written by VICTORIA SAXON

MASSIMILIANO NARCISO, and

ANDREA CAGOL

Designed by TONY FEJERAN

Not long ago in the kingdom of ARENDELLE, summer had arrived!

But it was winter inside the castle where Princesses 𝓔LSA and 𝒜NNA were playing. Elsa had **magical powers** and could create things out of snow and ice! She made a snowman named Olaf. Anna was delighted.

Then Elsa accidentally hurt Anna.

The king and queen rushed both girls
to the mystical trolls in the mountains.

The trolls cured Anna by **CHANGING HER MEMORIES** of Elsa's magic. They cautioned that others would fear Elsa's power. To help her control it, Elsa's parents gave her gloves.

With the castle gates closed, Elsa
stayed away from Anna – she never
wanted to hurt her again. But…

Elsa missed
ANNA.

Anna
missed
ELSA.

Years later, the king and queen were lost at sea. Without their parents, both princesses grew **LONELIER** and **LONELIER**.

Soon it was time for Elsa to take over as QUEEN. She was terrified that without her gloves, she might lose control of her powers in front of everyone!

Anna, on the other hand,
was excited to meet new people
– especially a prince named Hans.

THEY FELL
IN LOVE!

Elsa gathered all her courage to take
off her gloves and was successfully crowned
Queen of Arendelle!

With her gloves back on, Elsa proudly stood before her people.

But when Anna told Elsa that she wanted to marry Hans, Elsa forbade it. How could Anna want to marry a man she had only just met?

Frustrated, Anna tried to stop her sister and accidentally **PULLED OFF** one glove.

Without her glove and upset with Anna, Elsa accidentally **exposed** her secret powers. Ice and snow blasted from her hand, covering the kingdom.

Fearing she might hurt someone and ruin her kingdom, **ELSA FLED**.

Anna thought it was her fault Elsa's powers had been revealed. She rushed off to find her sister.

She hired a mountain man named Kristoff to be her guide.

In time, Anna and Kristoff found a snowman
named Olaf. He was alive!

Anna **REMEMBERED** him and the
good times she had shared with her sister.
Olaf led the way to Elsa.

Elsa was enjoying her time alone.

Now she was free to create whatever she wanted.

She built an ICE PALACE.

Anna begged Elsa to go home to thaw her frozen kingdom.
But Elsa feared she couldn't control her powers.

Angry and afraid, Elsa accidentally cast a
magic freezing spell on her little sister...

...and then created a **GIANT SNOWMAN.**
Anna and Kristoff ran. Olaf ran, too!

Anna's hair began to turn
white. Kristoff led her to the
trolls for help.

The trolls advised, 'Only an act of TRUE LOVE can thaw a frozen heart.'

Anna needed Hans for a true love's kiss!

Quickly,

Kristoff and Anna headed back to Arendelle.

When Anna found Hans, he **REFUSED** to kiss her. His plan all along had been to take over the kingdom. Anna was crushed!

Anna realized that Kristoff loved her! She needed all her strength to find him.

Meanwhile, Elsa had
returned to Arendelle to save
her kingdom. But now she was
in **TERRIBLE DANGER**.
When Anna saw Hans, she
knew what she had to do.

Anna
SAVED
Elsa.

It was an act of true love – true love
BETWEEN TWO SISTERS.

Soon the ice melted and Anna
realized she was in love with Kristoff.
As for Elsa, she became queen
again, a good queen who had learned
from her sister that LOVE was
the key to controlling her powers.

Treasure Cove Stories

Book list may be subject to change.